ISBN: 0-9742502-3-6

**Suggested Cataloging**
Turner, Ginger.
   Gold Mine! The California Gold Rush Story/ by Ginger Turner, Shekhar Shimpi
      p. cm. –  (The way people live)
   Summary: Describes the events surrounding the discovery of gold in California, the huge migration it brought to
   the area, the lifestyles of miners and mining towns.
   ISBN: 0-9742502-2-8
   LCCN: 2004107841
   1. California – Gold Discoveries – Juvenile literature.
   2. Frontier and pioneer life – California – Juvenile literature.
   3. Gold miners – California – Social life and customs – Juvenile literature.
   4. Mining camps – California – History – 19th century – Juvenile literature.
   I. Title. II. Series

History Research by Catherine Carlton

ATTENTION: SCHOOLS AND LIBRARIES
Quality discounts are available with quantity purchases for educational use.
For information, email info@gossamerbooks.com

http://www.gossamerbooks.com

# Gold Mine!

January 24, 1848.  *The banks of the Sacramento River.*

Heigh-Ho!

♪♪ Shout out for our gallant Rough and Ready... ♪♪

Ah, good morning, Mr Marshall. You're looking well--hey there, little fish!

Surprise!

I've got you now, little guy...

Hey, what's this?

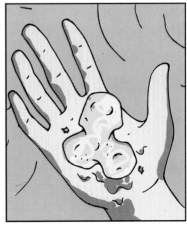

1

Four months later: May 1848
The small town of San Francisco

WOOOOOOO-

What's the rush, Sam?

--HOOOOOOO! Thank the Lord! Just wait till they see this!

Oops!

Ack!

?

Sam Brannan! Always causing trouble! What are you trying to sell us now?

GOLD! Gold in the American River!

Huh?!

I've just come from John Sutter's mill up the river...

You mean "Sutter's Folly"! What fool would go so far out into the wilderness?

I heard Mr. Brannan is planning to start a store out there himself!

And mighty glad I am. Look what I've found!

Whoah!

Dear me!

Oooo...

No touching, please!

But there's much more where this came from. That river is littered with gold everywhere!

There's enough to make us all very rich men. You don't have to do anything except go out there and stick your hands down into the stream.

Wait till the papers catch onto this...

February, 1849: Sutter's office.

There are three main ways for gold seekers to get to California.

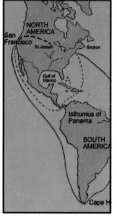

By ship...

Going by ship is easiest, but it takes 6 to 8 months.

Eight months!?!

They have to sail from New York all the way around Cape Horn, the southern tip of South America.

Another way is by both land and sea. They will take a ship south to the isthmus of Panama.

Then trek through the jungle to the Pacific Ocean on the other side, and take another ship north to San Francisco.

Oscar, can you move any faster?

The trek through the rainforest is dangerous, and the travelers are exposed to malaria and cholera!

And the third route?

Hey, Alice! Want to drive for a while?

Going overland the whole way. It should take only three months, maybe five.

The overland route will be most treacherous. Strange diseases, attacks from the hostile natives, heat and sweat, little food and lots of work. But they will come anyway. The lure of gold is too great for them to be scared away!

Thousands more will join them, from China, Brazil, Spain, Mexico,

I am glad I have a sister who is not afraid of adventures!

Charlie, do you think there are really pure gold nuggets lying on the banks of the rivers like pebbles?

That's what it says in John Fremont's guidebook. Even President Polk was talking about it. Any man who can get to California will surely make a fortune... So that's where we're going!

Oh, I come from New York City, with a... ♪♫

Getting there will be no small task. .... Yah!

washbowl on my knee. ♪♫ I'm bound for California, where a gold mine waits for me! Oh, Susannah! Don't you cry for me... ♪♫

September-October 1849. Monterrey, California.

Gentlemen, the eyes of all of civilized nations of the earth are turned towards us. Once a part of Mexico, we are now our own new land. We are gathered here to write the constitution of the future state of California.

Our two most important decisions will be on state borders and slavery.

California must be a slave state. Otherwise, thousands of freed slaves--the worst species of our population--will come to California, prepared to do nothing but steal or live on our charity.

I object to this slander! Free black men have just as good a right to come to California as white men.

Forget slavery! What about the Mexicans, Chinese, Spanish, French, Irish, Chileans, Germans, and Turks invading our state? They must be stopped perhaps we should have a special tax on foreign miners.

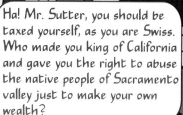

Ha! Mr. Sutter, you should be taxed yourself, as you are Swiss. Who made you king of California and gave you the right to abuse the native people of Sacramento valley just to make your own wealth?

Now that the Mexican-American war is over, California is no longer part of Mexico, General Vallejo. I have my freedom and will defend it until death. My freedom is nearly all I will have left after these newcomers rob my gold, my land, and my livelihood.

Just as you, an immigrant from Switzerland, enjoy your freedom, it should also be given to all immigrants--whether black, white, Mexican, Chinese, or New Yorker!

One year later. September 1850. Still on the trail...

I think the longer way would have been wiser.

But according to the guidebook, there was a shortcut around here somewhere.

Should we try to turn back the way we came, before we run out of food?

The oxen are too weak to go on right now.

Let's rest here and have the last of the biscuits ...

...then we can break the news to the others.

Charlie! Where did you put that knife?

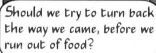

!

AAAH!

Where are you taking us? I demand to know!

Whoah, careful, that's a little too close for comfort.

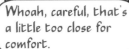

Does Fremont's guide book tell you where we are now?

Looks like a tribal meeting.

Doesn't anyone here speak English?

I do! What are you white folks doing way out here?

Gold rushers, no doubt. Newcomers are always causing trouble for the Crow.

These men stopped us on the road and brought us here.

What road? There's no path close to here.

Well, we got a little lost.

Ah, so you're following that old "shortcut." Ha, ha!

It seemed to be the easiest--

Nothing's easy out here in California.

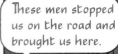

At least we've made it to California.

But I can make it easier--for a price. Why don't you follow yours truly, James Beckwourth, into the Sacramento Valley ... Or if you like, you can stay here and be scalped by these friendly gentlemen.

Sacramento, here we come.

Ten days later. Sacramento.

BRANNAN'S STORE

Here I'll leave you. Sam Brannan's store will provide you with plenty for the trip to San Francisco, or any other mining town along the way.

Thank you.

Beware the other troublemakers along the trail. There are many tribes throughout the gold country, and some are not as friendly as the Crow.

BRANNAN'S STO

I'll look inside for supplies. You check out the oxen.

But Mr. Brannan, I am sure you have a stronger fabric. These pants cannot survive an average day in the life of a miner. Isn't there anything sturdier and more practical?

Well Mr. Levi, that is all we have for the pants. If you like, you could look at the canvas rolls we have for stitching our tents...

Welcome, what can I do for you, miss?

Mr. Brannan, we need to furnish a new wagon.

If you can get that mule to move, I'll give him to you for free! He's no good to me.

Hmmm...

Mules love sugar, like men love gold --yum, irresistible.

Run and get it, Nugget!

There goes a free mule! Yee-haw!

Good riddance! And I hope he brings better luck to you. Heaven knows you'll need it out there. It ain't El Dorado for everyone.

Thank you, sir. I intend to find my own El Dorado. Good luck to you too.

Young man, wait...

A warning before you go ...

Listen and remember, because I have been there--I have seen the elephant--and I wish I never had...

Huh? What elephant?

Beware! California will not be as golden as you expect. In the untamed wilderness, you will find a challenge unlike any you have ever faced. What's your goal?

13

To find gold.

First, to stay alive! For centuries, gold has been man's obsession. To get it, he will stop at nothing--lying, stealing, cheating, and struggling halfway across the world.

Old man, I will remember you--but I will remember the gold in my pocket even better. California is calling--there is no other way.

Then I wish you good luck. But hang onto it tightly, for thousands of men are coming from all over the world. The foreigners are waiting to snatch it from you.

Alice, look what I've got. My first Nugget!

Come on, Mr. Sutter. I'll take you home.

What home, Harry? Everything I owned has been stolen from under my nose by these villain '49ers. My hard restless labors, everything I have risked my life for--ruined! What a great misfortune was this sudden discovery of gold for me.

Crazy man! Everyone else wants gold. That's why I gave away the secret!

October 1850: Grass Valley, one of the many boom towns along the way to Sacramento River.

Look, Alice, we've finally made it!

I can't wait to get my hands on a shovel and start digging. Just imagine--All those nuggets just waiting to be picked up at the water's edge. We'll soon have everything in gold. Gold necklaces for you. Gold watches for me. Gold! Gold! Gold!

Gold pie pans?

If it's so easy to get rich out here, why are so many people still living in tents?

Once they get their gold, they go back home, of course. No one actually lives in California.

Well, this is my home now, so I intend to live well.

That evening...

Whoops!

Excuse me, sir. Which way to the gold digging?

Ha-ha! You must be joking!

What can I do for you, miss?

Could I have a glass of water please?

Certainly. That water will be five dollars.

FIVE DOLLARS!?!

CRASH

Oh, sorry, sir! I'm just surprised that--well, if water is five dollars, then how much is dinner?

I'm afraid this place may be too expensive for me.

Everything costs more out here in gold country, miss.

You must be new here. I'm Mart Taylor, but you can call me Mart.

Let me give you this water on the house.

Thank you.

?

Oh, excuse me for staring, Miss. It's just, we don't see women very often around here.

Gold! The Mother Lode!

What?

So much that I could pluck it off the ground with my bare hands like pebbles.

Where did you find it, sir?

All I need is a few extra hands to help me carry it back. A gold mine, boy! I need a business partner to help me dig up the claim.

I've just arrived, and I'm aiming to mine just such a claim. Let me help you.

I need a mule-- a good sturdy young mule.

I've just bought a mule. He's outside ready to go now if you--

Hold it!

Huh?

Don't go any further, Peg Leg-- you old scoundrel.

I'm just helping this new man get acquainted with the territory.

You get out of here, Peg Leg. Stop pestering this poor boy!

I'm not making any trouble. This boy's gonna help me get to my gold.

Yes, I'm--

No, he's not. Now scram!

Well, good luck to you, boy.

Hey, why did you--

Don't listen to him. He's been trying to trick new arrivals for years.

What about his gold mine?

It's just a hallucination he had once when he got lost out in the desert.

Mart and I found him passed out on a rock miles away from town.

He was a sorry sight.

We thought he was dead, but when he came to, he kept mumbling that he could see gold all around where there was none.

He's been searching for it ever since.

Why don't you let me show you around?

Thank you, sir!

I'm Charlie Green.

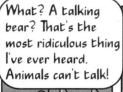

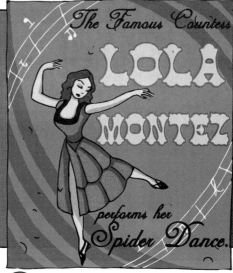

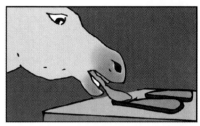

Later, back in town.

SALOON

It's four long years since I reached this land, in search among the rocks and sand... ♪ ♪

And yet I'm poor when the truth is told. I'm a lousy miner in search of shining gold.

Oh, hello, Oscar. Mind if I warm my hands?

Evening, Charlie. Join in!

Thanks for your help today.

You're mighty welcome. Just help me back if you ever get the chance. Say, where you from, Charlie?

New York City. Have you ever met anyone else from there?

No, but you could tell me you were from the stars and I wouldn't know the difference, would I?

No, I suppose not.

That's the beauty of California. No one knows your past, so you can be whomever and whatever you want. It's a fresh beginning. No one can stop you from doing what you want to do... even if you used to be a slave, like me.

Slave?! How did you get all the way out here?

My master brought me from New Orleans--first on a boat to Panama, then trekking through the thickest jungles I've ever laid eyes on, and onto another ship up to San Francisco.

A long trip.

But what my master didn't realize was that, as soon as we ended up on free soil in California-- it was against the law for him to keep slaves!

23

Oscar! Come quick. The Spider is in Taylor's saloon tonight.

What spider?

Come on, Charlie. You can come too.

Wow! What a great place!

I'm celebrating tonight, boys! My three hundredth night with no gold mine!

I'll see the elephant now... ♫ ♪

Why do you just stand there?

Oh, they wouldn't want us in there. You can go in if you like, Charlie.

Nonsense. You're coming in with me.

Hello, there! It's Mr. Charlie, the newcomer, fresh after his first day of mining. Come in and have a drink, on the house!

Thank you, Mr. Taylor. I'll buy drinks for these two fellas as well.

Well... okay, I guess, if they are with you.

You say you're driving the coach now, Sam?

That's right!

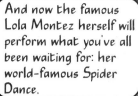
Attention, everyone!

And now the famous Lola Montez herself will perform what you've all been waiting for: her world-famous Spider Dance.

I've been waiting for this all week!

Amazing!

Wow!

Lola is a crazy woman--dresses like a man, smokes cigars, owns a pet grizzly bear--but out here in the wilderness, there's no one to stop her.

CRASH

Hey! Watch out, you almost hit me!

Don't grab him like that!

Get out of here! This ain't your place.

Out of my way!

Hey, watch it there, Sam. Don't get too rough in my saloon.

28

Sniff
Sniff

Oh, Nugget, this doesn't look good!

Don't try to move him yet... Please let him be okay. I should have waited for him.

He's still breathing!

Later that day. Alice's tent.

That's all right. I'm making enough money for both of us. I've almost made enough to buy some land and build us a house in town.

Hey, Charlie. What happened to you?

I failed. Six months in California, and I've got nothing but dust.

Here is your order. Three slices of apple pie.

Hey Alice! Can I buy one of those famous pies?

Your pies are as good as gold!

I'm finished with mining. Let's go back home.

We ARE home.

No, I mean back to New York. I'm sick of this place. There's no gold left here.

Are you crazy? I'd rather be trampled by an elephant.

Hmm... there's only one last option for me.

Later that day. Taylor's saloon.

Pity, she will surely be missed.

Mr. Taylor, I'm afraid little Lotta won't be singing and dancing anymore in the saloon. She's leaving for the New York stage.

There is something else I want to tell you...

One night, a few months ago, a dirty, wounded man came to my door. I was scared beyond belief, but you know I always have a policy to help those in need. I took him in and cared for him without question.

I think that Sam's stagecoach is in grave danger!

I kept thinking I had seen his face somewhere before. But after that night, I never saw him again... until yesterday.

What does this mean?

I got a good look at his face that night, and there's something you should know.

Later that day. At the mines...

Hello? Is anyone here?

Oh! How do you do, miss?

Have you seen Charlie? I've brought his lunch. Hopefully, it will cheer him up.

No, ma'am. I haven't seen him all day.

Strange... He comes here every day.

He said something about going to find the elephant.

Meanwhile, many miles out in the wilderness...

Are we getting closer?

I think it's just around this next bend.

That's what you said three bends ago.

Whew! You sure are speedy for a man with only one leg.

I'm not sure how much longer I can walk in this midday heat.

Just over the hill. I know I recognize that tree.

Four hours later...

Peg Leg, I'm finished. Just take me back to town.

I would be glad to--but I'm not sure which way it is...

TAP TAP

Maybe I'm hearing things, but it sounds like horse hooves riding this way.

Peg Leg, you stay there. I'll check it out!

Take that!

Charlie! Are you okay? That guy was about to--

Alice! Where did you come from? Oscar?

Lu told us you had gone out with Peg Leg, so we followed your tracks. You guys have been going in circles for a while. We were worried when we heard that Joaquin Murieta and his bandits were attacking stage coaches in the area. Sheriff Love has sworn to catch Joaquin and bring back his head.

The sheriff is probably somewhere around here right now. He won't let those other bandits escape.

Oh! Charlie, I feel so guilty. I've never killed a man before.

Don't worry--It's not your fault! You did what you had to do.

... there, there-- it's okay!

Ahem... There was no other way. He might have killed me!

It's too sad! I can't look at him.

Nugget, I think it's safe to go down now.

But, we've come so far...

Well, Nugget, I guess maybe that gold mine I saw really was my imagination.

...We can't turn back now!

*That night...*

More beautiful than ever, Lola!

Let's celebrate, sister! We can beat Lola's Spider Dance any day!

Where's Max tonight?

Good evening, gentlemen!

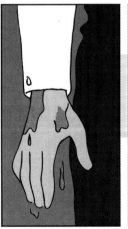

Sheriff Love!

It is over. Joaquin Murieta has been captured and killed. His reign of terror is ended.

Hurrah!

It can't be true! I thought he got away. He was so close. Now, I'll never see him again!

Excuse me, Sheriff. Did you say you got Murieta?

We caught two Mexican bandits outside Sacramento tonight. We believe one of them was Murieta.

How can you be sure?

Twenty-seven years later. June 1880.

Stop the carriage!

That man looks familiar...

Today is a great day for Dong Metallurgies. I remember when I was a young immigrant building other people's tools. Now I use the tools myself...

Yes, sir, congratulations on your biggest client yet!

Let's make sure we get the order for Mr. Stanford out on time. This railroad will be only the beginning of California's great future --and we can't be late!

And I think over there is the spot where I used to dance...

Can I help you?

Um, maybe I have the wrong place. I'm looking for Taylor's saloon.

I'm sorry, miss. Taylor's saloon has been closed for twenty years.

Huh?

But my husband Mart Taylor is sitting right over there. Would you like a menu?

I just wanted to see my old home. I used to dance here... I was looking for someone too, but I guess he's not here anymore.

Hey, wait, you look familiar. What did you say your name was?

Lotta Crabtree.

Alice, can we have another round here?

That's it! The little elephant he gave me. Lola told me it was worn by a mythical bandit, but I thought he was killed many years ago...

Oh, that's just my old friend Max. And "seeing the elephant" is an old miner's expression--it means going through everything, good and bad, and coming out on the other side. That's California for you, land of pioneers and entrepreneurs. You never know who you'll meet...

... or who you'll become.

Gee, I can't believe you're the same little Lotta Crabtree that used to dance here. You're just about the most famous woman in the country now!

Maybe Lola was right and he is still alive...

It all started here, with Lola's lessons in Mart's saloon! Well, I must get back to New York.

I guess it couldn't be the same one... or could it?

Some say Sheriff Love caught Joaquin red-handed. Others claim he made a mistake and killed the wrong man. But most believe Joaquin Murieta was only a figment of our imaginations...

But we know the real story, don't we, Charlie?

The End

42

# Fact or Fiction

Even though the characters of Charlie and Alice were not real, their lives are based on true historical accounts.

### Did water really cost five dollars?

Yes, some miners even paid $100! Most '49ers were not prepared for the hot, dry climate, so California businessmen took advantage of their thirst. Because so many people were moving west and could not carry all the water they needed with them, there was a high demand and low supply of water.

### How many women were in the mining towns?

In the 1850s, men outnumbered women in California by 10 to 1. Despite their small numbers, women still participated in every aspect of mining town life, becoming successful miners, storekeepers, gamblers, cooks, muleteers, and actresses, among others. The low number of women meant that their skills of housekeeping and cooking were in especially high demand, and many women made more money from these services than their husbands did from mining. Money allowed some California women to become more independent than they could have been at home.

### A gold mine can't get up and walk away. How could Peg Leg lose his mine?

Legends of lost mines circulating during the Gold Rush were actually an important factor in enticing curious prospectors westward. In 1827, a horse trader named Thomas Smith took a short cut and got lost. Climbing a small hill, he found its top covered with shiny pebbles. He put a few handfuls into his saddle bags and forgot about the hill. Smith, who had lost a leg and got the nickname "Peg Leg," later sold his solid gold pebbles for $2,000 in San Francisco. He never could find his way back to the mine, and the Lost Peg Leg Mine became a western legend.

*Want to know more? You can find out about the real characters in the Gold Rush and California history in your local library, on the Internet, or at Gossamer Books LLC web site at http://www.gossamerbooks.com*

# Who Went Where?

Many of the people Charlie and Alice met really existed. Who were some of the real characters, and what happened to them after the book ended?

### Joaquin Murieta

Although most historians agree that Joaquin did exist, no one knows the whole story. Like most Mexican and Chinese miners, Murieta was probably forced off his claim by the 1852 Foreign Miners' Tax. But legend says it was not until vigilantes killed Joaquin's family for a crime he didn't commit that Joaquin decided to form a gang of bandits to get revenge. By the time Sheriff Harry Love killed two Mexicans in July 1853, several bandit gangs had sprung up, and no one could be sure of their true identities. To collect his $1,000 reward, the Sheriff displayed the severed head and hand of the two men he called Joaquin Murieta and Three-Fingered Jack…meanwhile, the real Joaquin probably lived on anonymously.

### Lotta Crabtree

At the age of eight, Lotta began dancing in Mart Taylor's saloon in Grass Valley, where her father was a gold digger. Her mother soon found that Lotta's feisty dancing, following in the footsteps of her mentor Lola Montez, could make more money than her father's mining. From the vaudeville stages of San Francisco, Lotta moved to New York, where she became Broadway's highest paid star. One of the most famous and adored actresses of the 19th century, Lotta always remained connected to her Gold Rush roots and made several return visits to San Francisco.

### James Beckwourth

Born a black slave in Virginia, Beckwourth gained his freedom and signed up as a fur trapper for a westward expedition to the Rocky Mountains in 1824. Known for his hilarious storytelling and his sense of adventure, he was adopted by the Crow Indian tribe and lived with them for almost eight years, becoming a Crow warrior and marrying and abandoning several Crow women. Serving as one of the most important trail guides in the Gold Rush was just one small part of the life of this famous American mountain man.